Dear Reader,

Welcome to a fun-filled book of acrostic poems!

Here at Young Writers, we are delighted to introduce our new poetry competition for KS1 pupils, *My First Acrostic: Animal Adventures*. Acrostic poems are an enjoyable way to introduce pupils to the world of poetry and allow the young writer to open their imagination to a range of topics of their choice. The colourful and engaging entry forms allowed even the youngest (or most reluctant) of pupils to create a poem using the acrostic technique and with that, encouraged them to include other literary techniques such as similes and description. Here at Young Writers we are passionate about introducing the love and art of creative writing to the next generation and we love being a part of their journey.

From the jungle to the ocean, pets to mythical monsters, these pupils take you on a journey through the animal kingdom and showcase their budding creativity along the way. So we invite you to dive into these pages and take a glimpse into these blossoming young writers' minds. We hope you will relish these roarsome poems as much as we have.

Contents

All Saints CE Primary School, Wigston Magna

William Johnson (8)	1
Skyla Faulkner-Bollen (6)	2
Kaitlynn Kemp (6)	3
Sukhmani Sarao (6)	4
Nawaf Althurwi (5)	5

Cookstown Primary School, Coolnafranky Demesne

Rylee Armstrong (6)	6
Lara Patterson (6)	7
Isabella Forrest (5)	8
Ava-Grace Robinson (6)	9
Harry Evans (5)	10
Mabelle Erskine (6)	11
Matthew Orr (6)	12
Rachel Gourley (5)	13
Caleb Cuddy (5)	14

Denham Green Primary Academy, Denham Green

Nathan Grant (5)	15
Ruby Pearson (5)	16
Dylan Tuffin (4)	17

Filton Avenue Primary School, Horfield

Olive Deveraux (7)	18
Tristan Pedrick (6)	19
Jesse Chung (7)	20
Yahya Chaudhry	21

Gourdon Primary School, Gourdon

Ollie Campbell (7)	22
Taylor Gibson (7)	23

Grace Mary Primary School, Oldbury

Charles Healy (7)	24
Havya Shah (7)	25
Rose Andrews (6)	26
Sahib Sandhu (7)	27

Lime Academy Parnwell, Parnwell

Oliver Robinson (6)	28
Gabriel Zareba (5)	29
Georgie-Rose Ward-Regan (5)	30
Zahra Ouail (6)	31
Lucyna Szymecka (5)	32
Danielius Blinka (5)	33
Emmanuel Francis (6)	34

Martin Frobisher Infant School, Altofts

Theo Tasou (6)	35
Claudia Wilson (6)	36
Marley Barker (7)	37
Poppy Southernwood (6)	38
Lois Kirk (5)	39
Henry Gilbert (6)	40
Holly Murray (6)	41
Amelia Jackson (6)	42
Molly Armitage (6)	43
Abigail Plumb (6)	44

Jack Myers (7)	45
Archie Swift (5)	46
Scarlett Talbot (6)	47
Issabelle Stokes (6)	48
Oliver Addison (6)	49
Carla Wolliter (6)	50
Isla Andrew (5)	51
Billy Bryant (6)	52
Max Harper (6)	53
Harrison Joe Harman-Senior (6)	54
Amelia Allington (5)	55
Isaac Davies (6)	56
Riley Carter (7)	57
Desmond Marciniak (6)	58
Tyler Slack (7)	59
Sofia Naseer (6)	60
Brooke Hudson (7)	61
Kadie Pearson (6)	62
Beau Bellwood (6)	63
Kaia (5)	64
Bethany Hanmer (6)	65
Marcus Moran (6)	66
Betty Jones (5)	67
Darcie Spencer (5)	68

Mount Nod Primary School, Coventry

Braeden Dunlop (7)	69
Gabriella Nutt (7)	70
Iona O'Donnell (6)	71
Haydn Lewis (7)	72
Evie Howard (7)	73
Isaac Mills (7)	74
Jai Singh Kaila (6)	75
Nishān Kaur Kaila (6)	76
Leah Allchurch (5)	77
Jenson Cole (6)	78

Pelham Primary School, Bexleyheath

Sanya Khatri (5)	79
Mila Dhesi (4)	80

Jack Brown (4)	81

Perry Court E-ACT Academy, Hengrove

Sienna Walker (7)	82
Bonnie Firks (7)	83
Miley McSweeney (7)	84
Layla Stuckes (6)	85
Joelle Forbes (6)	86
Eva Massaro (6)	87

Richard Hill CE Primary School, Thurcaston

Ella Fosberry (7)	88
Bethany Kendall (7)	89
Noah Jackson (7)	90
Jacob Bailey (6)	91
Finn Baker (6)	92
Oscar Bower (7)	93
Zak Foster (7)	94
Lola Fletcher (7)	95
Joshua Little (7)	96
Madison Burbidge (6)	97
Isobel Richardson (6)	98
Bella Culleton (7)	99

Singleton CE Primary School, Singleton

Mathilda Jewitt (5)	100
Gretta Mills (4)	101
Noah North (5)	102
Arthur (6)	103

St Chad's RC Primary School, South Norwood

Jayrell K. Agyapong (6)	104
Rocio Navarro (7)	105
Natalia Gorka (5)	106
Angel Ava Agyekum (6)	107
Chanelle Appiah Arhin (5)	108
Jessica Anene (5)	109

St George's School Edgbaston, Edgbaston

Jaime Blanch (6) 110
Sophia Buray (7) 111
Yuna Isobe (5) 112

St Mary's Lewisham CE Primary School, Lewisham

Khaeleam Darlington (7) 113
Te'Amo Williams-Dythe (5) 114

St Michael's RC Primary School, Pillgwenlly

Pola Sochacka (6) 115
Theo Scarpato-Hughes (7) 116
Lithongo Ndololwana (7) 117
Mateusz Ukrynczuk (7) 118

St Peter's CE (A) Primary School, Caverswall

Jacob Bainbridge (5) 119
Archie Walker (6) 120
Kaiden Rushton (6) 121
Benjamin Coggan (6) 122
Maisy Hague (5) 123

St Peter's CIW Primary School, Rossett

Megan Dawes (6) 124
Zoe Sutherland (7) 125
Lillie Walsh (7) 126
Harry Bueruer (6) 127
Jack Yiend (6) 128

Thomas Wolsey Ormiston Academy, Ipswich

Zoe Hall (8) 129
Jay Walters (8) 130
Chloe Barden (6) 131

Alice Wade (9) 132

Whitehouse Primary School, Elm Tree

Alice Tali Taylor (6) 133
Isla Harker (6) 134
Lillia Yau (6) 135
Thomas Amos (5) 136
Jacob Ragan (5) 137
Noah Wassell (5) 138
Ted Swainston (6) 139
Haider Ali Khan (5) 140
Noah McDonald (6) 141
Isaac Fixter (5) 142
Isla Archment (5) 143
Georgie Huskinson-Williams (5) 144
Emily Buttle (6) 145
Zayn-Ali Ayoub (6) 146
Billy (7) 147
Hafeez Khan (6) 148
Leo Atkinson (5) 149
Dominic White (6), Daisy & Reece Fletcher (5) 150
Alec Fixter (5) 151
Teddy Moore (6) 152
Lucy Coyne (5) 153
Jake Cordiner (5) 154
Phrel Oketunde (6) 155
Macie Graham (5) 156

Woodlands School, Great Warley

Bhavraj Sokhal (6) 157
Millie Patel (6) 158
Leo Sheringham (6) 159
Kiaran Pagotre (7) 160
Veer Singh Virk (6) 161

The Poems

Monkey

M esses around in cages
O nly stops for bananas
N aughty most of the time
K eeps on climbing
E nergy slowly runs out
Y awn, time for bed.

William Johnson (8)
All Saints CE Primary School, Wigston Magna

Unicorn

U nusual
N ice
I nteresting
C ute
O dd
R ainbow
N umber one.

Skyla Faulkner-Bollen (6)
All Saints CE Primary School, Wigston Magna

Unicorn

U nusual
N ice
I nteresting
C asual
O ld
R ainbow
N oisy.

Kaitlynn Kemp (6)
All Saints CE Primary School, Wigston Magna

Unicorn

U nusual
N ice
I mpatient
C ool
O ld
R unning
N aughty.

Sukhmani Sarao (6)
All Saints CE Primary School, Wigston Magna

Crab

C razy
R ed
A mazing
B usy.

Nawaf Althurwi (5)
All Saints CE Primary School, Wigston Magna

Happy Hippos

H ippos are herbivores
I n water is where they love to be
P aige is what I would call a pet hippo
P ygmy is a type of hippo
O tters love water like hippos do
P ink is the colour of hippo milk
O ver 35 years is how long a hippo lives
T hey come out of water to eat
A frica is where hippos chill out
M assive: the size of a hippo
U sually hippos have just one baby
S unset is when they come out of water.

Rylee Armstrong (6)
Cookstown Primary School, Coolnafranky Demesne

Butterfly

B eautiful wings
U sually love to fly
T eeth to chew out of the shell
T rying to eat a lot of plants
E ach time, it sheds its skin
R eaches a spot to make a chrysalis
F orms wings
L eaves chrysalis as a butterfly
Y oung caterpillar is gone, now it is a butterfly.

Lara Patterson (6)
Cookstown Primary School, Coolnafranky Demesne

Bella's Butterfly

B utterflies go unnoticed
U nless you really look!
T iny, little creatures
T entacles on their head
E very garden has them
R eally take a look!
F lutter after flutter
L anding at your feet!
Y ellow, pink, blue and other colours too.

Isabella Forrest (5)
Cookstown Primary School, Coolnafranky Demesne

My African Elephant

E ars so big to keep cool
L ong trunk for
E ating, drinking, throwing too
P lay is what they love to do
H elping their young
A sian and African elephants
N oisy when they blow their trunks
T usks made from ivory.

Ava-Grace Robinson (6)
Cookstown Primary School, Coolnafranky Demesne

Dinosaurs Roar

D inosaurs are cool
I n the water, making
N oisy splashes
O h dear, it's coming
S hhhh!
A rghhhh! It sees me, hide
U nder this rock
R oar!

Harry Evans (5)
Cookstown Primary School, Coolnafranky Demesne

The Flying Unicorn

U p in the sky
N ight-time flying
I n the moonlight
C hanging colours
O range, then blue
R ainbows and friends
N ow and always.

Mabelle Erskine (6)
Cookstown Primary School, Coolnafranky Demesne

King Of The Jungle

L ives in a cave or in the zoo
I love watching The Lion Guard
O range and yellow with fluffy hair like a blanket
N o touching, it has sharp claws!

Matthew Orr (6)
Cookstown Primary School, Coolnafranky Demesne

The Horse

H ot days with my horse
O n the beach
R unning on the sand
S un shining
E njoying ourselves.

Rachel Gourley (5)
Cookstown Primary School, Coolnafranky Demesne

Tiger

T igers are strong
I like tigers
G o and look at their teeth
E veryone is scared
R oar!

Caleb Cuddy (5)
Cookstown Primary School, Coolnafranky Demesne

The Unfriendly Dinosaur

D eadly, dangerous
I nteresting fossils
N ot alive anymore
O ld bones
S uper scary
A nkylosaurus
U nfriendly
R oars loudly!

Nathan Grant (5)
Denham Green Primary Academy, Denham Green

My Unicorn Friend

U ndeniably cute
N aturally
I nteresting
C olourful
O r just
R eally
N ice!

Ruby Pearson (5)
Denham Green Primary Academy, Denham Green

Oscar The Dog

D oes good tricks
O scar is his name
G ives good hugs.

Dylan Tuffin (4)
Denham Green Primary Academy, Denham Green

The Naughty Kitten

K ittens are small
I know my kitten, Mitten
T he craziest of all
T oday, I found my Mitten playing ball
E very kitten enjoys cricket!
N aughty naughty Mitten the Kitten.

Olive Deveraux (7)
Filton Avenue Primary School, Horfield

Monkey

M y bananas
O r apples
N o carrots
K eep bananas for me
E ats bananas
Y ummy bananas!

Tristan Pedrick (6)
Filton Avenue Primary School, Horfield

The Wolf

W olves are deadly hunters
O ften, wolves howl loud
L ovely cubs, cute and happy
F ast to catch their prey.

Jesse Chung (7)
Filton Avenue Primary School, Horfield

Cat

C an you run?
A nd can you walk?
T each your cat?

Yahya Chaudhry
Filton Avenue Primary School, Horfield

Tigers

T igers are fierce but they are cute as well
I n the jungle, they run fast
G reat big sharp claws
E very time, tigers stripes are different
R oaring across the jungle
S caring the parrots, making them screech.

Ollie Campbell (7)
Gourdon Primary School, Gourdon

The Bear

B ig and scary like a monster
E ats honey and fish
A nybody who kicks a bear is crazy
R un, run as fast as the wind if you see one
S tay away because it is safer.

Taylor Gibson (7)
Gourdon Primary School, Gourdon

Mountain Lions

M ountain lions are mysterious
O ut in cold mountains
U npredictable
N ot as tall as normal lions
T hey eat meat all day long, how greedy!
A ggressive as a bull
I s a huge animal, an enormous cat
N ot nice, not nice at all

L ikes jumping and playing in the sun
I t likes to hunt and play with its food
O MG, they are scary
N ot afraid of nature.

Charles Healy (7)
Grace Mary Primary School, Oldbury

Giant Panda

G ood swimmers
I ncredibly slow
A lways eating bamboo, how greedy!
N ever stop eating, bamboo is their favourite
T hreatened animals, they could be extinct very soon.

P retty plump
A sian animals
N ot a small bear
D istinctive black and white face
A lways unique.

Havya Shah (7)
Grace Mary Primary School, Oldbury

Giant Panda

G obbles bamboo all day
I ncredibly lazy
A ggressive and as brave as a soldier
N ever stop gobbling food
T hick black fur.

P retty plump, a cuddly, fluffy bear
A sian animal
N ot a small bear
D id you know they are hunted?
A ttitude is the best.

Rose Andrews (6)
Grace Mary Primary School, Oldbury

Jaguar

J aguars live to be twelve years old
A merica has up to 64,000 jaguars
G allop at pace after their prey
U nique fur
A lmost completely extinct
R oar loud because they're going to fight!

Sahib Sandhu (7)
Grace Mary Primary School, Oldbury

Slow Sloth

S low, sharp nails, sleepy, sad
L azy, long arms, long legs
O n trees, omnivorous
T hey eat meat
H appy sloth.

Oliver Robinson (6)
Lime Academy Parnwell, Parnwell

Frog

F rogs are green
R ibbit ribbit frog sound
O ut from the eggs
G oing to sit on the lily pad.

Gabriel Zareba (5)
Lime Academy Parnwell, Parnwell

Sleepy Sloth

S loths are hungry
L ong legs
O n trees
T hey eat fruit
H anging.

Georgie-Rose Ward-Regan (5)
Lime Academy Parnwell, Parnwell

Sloths

S loths are cute
L azy
O n the trees
T ree dwellers
H anging.

Zahra Ouail (6)
Lime Academy Parnwell, Parnwell

Frog

F unny frog
R ed eyes
O n the pond
G reen body.

Lucyna Szymecka (5)
Lime Academy Parnwell, Parnwell

Fabulous Frogs

F unny
R ed eyes
O range feet
G rass hoppers.

Danielius Blinka (5)
Lime Academy Parnwell, Parnwell

Treefrog

F rogs do jump
R ed eyes
O range feet
G reen.

Emmanuel Francis (6)
Lime Academy Parnwell, Parnwell

A Giraffe's Adventure

G iraffes have brown spots like mud patches
I n the zoo, they live and play
R eally tall necks like tall skyscrapers
A mazingly tall neck to reach leaves from trees
F luffy fur that is brown and yellow
F un and furry yellow
E ach giraffe likes eating leaves
S uper long tongue.

Theo Tasou (6)
Martin Frobisher Infant School, Altofts

Elephant

E lephants are very large animals
L akes are where they get their drink
E lephants are the biggest animals on land
P air of tusks
H air is on the very top of the elephant's head
A n elephant is grey
N o other animal is as big
T usks are to catch their prey.

Claudia Wilson (6)
Martin Frobisher Infant School, Altofts

Cool Unicorns

U nicorns are beautiful and magical
N ormally, unicorns are cool
I live in the enchanted forest
C an fly very fast
O riginal unicorns look pretty
R eally, really colourful unicorn
N o other animals can be like a unicorn.

Marley Barker (7)
Martin Frobisher Infant School, Altofts

The Fantastic Dolphins

D olphins live in a dark, blue sea
O cean is good for dolphins
L ying on the cool sea
P ouncing over the shiny water
H urdling over the showy water
I deal in the beautiful waves
N ice and nasty dolphins, they swim.

Poppy Southernwood (6)
Martin Frobisher Infant School, Altofts

Unicorn's Life Is Magic

U nicorns are great
N obody has ever seen one
I n a magical forest, a mist appears
C ute and fluffy, also cuddly
O n its head, it's got a horn
R eally colourful
N ever seen again.

Lois Kirk (5)
Martin Frobisher Infant School, Altofts

Unicorn

U nicorns are made for fun
N ice and shiny
I nstead of hands, they have hooves
C an't catch a ball
O ften comes from the woods
R eady to go
N eat hooves at their feet.

Henry Gilbert (6)
Martin Frobisher Infant School, Altofts

Cute Puppy

P uppies are small and they are babies
U sually, we growl for some time
P uppies are cute dogs, they can't see until ten weeks
P layful puppy plays with dog toys
Y ap yap yap!

Holly Murray (6)
Martin Frobisher Infant School, Altofts

A Unicorn's Life

U nicorns are cool
N ice unicorns
I t has a horn and wings
C olourful mane and tail
O range, pink and yellow
R ainbows and stars
N ever see them.

Amelia Jackson (6)
Martin Frobisher Infant School, Altofts

A Turtle's Life

T urtles have hard shells
U nder the sea, they swim
R eally slow
T urtles live under the sea
L aying eggs on the sand
E ggs crack and babies are born.

Molly Armitage (6)
Martin Frobisher Infant School, Altofts

Cat

C ute, fantastic cats are playing in the snow for their first time
A dult cats are tall and fantastic
T all cats climb up trees so you can see them in the distance.

Abigail Plumb (6)
Martin Frobisher Infant School, Altofts

Raptor

R aptors are rushy
A mazing creatures
P ushes his friends
T alented little raptor
O ften lived in the jungle
R uler of the jungle.

Jack Myers (7)
Martin Frobisher Infant School, Altofts

Chicken

C lucking chickens
H atching eggs
I n the hen house
C luck! Cluck!
K eep them safe
E ggs, eggs
N ow we eat the eggs.

Archie Swift (5)
Martin Frobisher Infant School, Altofts

A Rabbit's Tail

R abbits are so soft
A re rabbits cute?
B ig rabbits can hop
B ig rabbits are nice
I n the rabbit cage
T he rabbits are brown.

Scarlett Talbot (6)
Martin Frobisher Infant School, Altofts

Dolphin

D ives in the sea
O ver the waves
L ives in the sea
P lays with other animals
H unts for food
I t is big
N o legs.

Issabelle Stokes (6)
Martin Frobisher Infant School, Altofts

Lion

L ies on a plank of wood in a sunny spot
I mpossible to find a lion in Africa
O nce, a lion ate a plant
N o lion can run faster than a cheetah.

Oliver Addison (6)
Martin Frobisher Infant School, Altofts

A Turtle's Life

T urtles live in water
U nder the sea they play
R eally cute
T urtles are great to me
L ive in the sea
E at salad.

Carla Wolliter (6)
Martin Frobisher Infant School, Altofts

Dolphin

D ive
O ver the waves
L ives in the water
P lays
H unting for food
I t is swimming
N o legs.

Isla Andrew (5)
Martin Frobisher Infant School, Altofts

Fantastic Humans

H umans live in houses
U ncles are nice to me
M en are nice
A man is strong
N o other animals are like people.

Billy Bryant (6)
Martin Frobisher Infant School, Altofts

A Camel's Life

C amels are cute
A ll over the world
M oving for a long time
E very camel has two humps
L icking plants.

Max Harper (6)
Martin Frobisher Infant School, Altofts

T-Rex

T hey only eat meat
R eally scarier than any dinosaur on the planet
E very dinosaur is weaker than T-rex
e **X** tinct.

Harrison Joe Harman-Senior (6)
Martin Frobisher Infant School, Altofts

Dog's Life

D ogs are great friends to people
O n walks, they run really fast
G reat, soft fur
S ome dogs chase their tails.

Amelia Allington (5)
Martin Frobisher Infant School, Altofts

Dog

D ogs are my friends - dogs of all kinds
O ver 1000 dogs I like
G reat dogs are my favourite because they can do tricks.

Isaac Davies (6)
Martin Frobisher Infant School, Altofts

Sharks

S harks eat fish
H ard to look after
A lways causing trouble
R un away!
K illers in the sea

Riley Carter (7)
Martin Frobisher Infant School, Altofts

Lion

L ions have long, sharp teeth
I n the jungle
O ften, they roar
N ow it is time to hunt for food.

Desmond Marciniak (6)
Martin Frobisher Infant School, Altofts

A Dog's Life

D ogs are cute
O n a morning, we cuddle
G oing for walks
S wim in the water.

Tyler Slack (7)
Martin Frobisher Infant School, Altofts

Shark

S wim
H unting for food
A ctually scary
R IP
K ill you.

Sofia Naseer (6)
Martin Frobisher Infant School, Altofts

Cat

C ats are lots of fun
A nimals are beautiful
T ry not to hurt animals.

Brooke Hudson (7)
Martin Frobisher Infant School, Altofts

Cat

C ats like balls
A nd like to go to sleep
T ails are long and black.

Kadie Pearson (6)
Martin Frobisher Infant School, Altofts

Cat

C ats play with balls
A nd they chase mice
T ails are floppy.

Beau Bellwood (6)
Martin Frobisher Infant School, Altofts

Dog

D ogs can run a lot
O ver the puddles and get wet
G et balls.

Kaia (5)
Martin Frobisher Infant School, Altofts

Dog's Life

D ogs are cute and fluffy
O ur dog is big
G oing for a walk.

Bethany Hanmer (6)
Martin Frobisher Infant School, Altofts

A Dog's Life

D ogs are fluffy
O n a morning, I walk the dogs
G reat dogs.

Marcus Moran (6)
Martin Frobisher Infant School, Altofts

Dog

D og has a bone
O n a lead
G one! Run away.

Betty Jones (5)
Martin Frobisher Infant School, Altofts

Dog

D ig for food
O ver logs
G et treats.

Darcie Spencer (5)
Martin Frobisher Infant School, Altofts

Oliver

O liver the orange orangutan jumping high
R ight under the night sky
A good friend
N ever never stop jumping
G o! Go! Go! He is so strong!
U nder and over the trees he goes
T ime to see his animal friends, "Hello!"
A nd the swinging never ends
N ight night jungle and my hairy friends!

Braeden Dunlop (7)
Mount Nod Primary School, Coventry

Facts About Dolphins

D olphins are grey
O ceans are dolphin's homes
L argest ocean dolphins are the orca, pilot whale and false killer whale
P oorly dolphins
H armless dolphins
I rrawaddy dolphin
N orthern right whale dolphin
S outhern right whale dolphin.

Gabriella Nutt (7)
Mount Nod Primary School, Coventry

Life Of Squirrel

S mall, furry squirrels
Q uickly scamper about
U p and down the trees
I like the name 'squirrel'
R unning here and there
R ed in Scotland and can be rare
E ating yummy nuts whilst
L ong, bushy tails sway.

Iona O'Donnell (6)
Mount Nod Primary School, Coventry

Leo The Leopard

L eo is a leopard
E normous claws, big paws
O range fur with spots on
P ointy, sharp teeth
A t night, they hunt
R unning so fast
D on't be scared, he is just a big cat.

Haydn Lewis (7)
Mount Nod Primary School, Coventry

Tigers

T igers sneak up on their prey
I nsects crawl on the tiger's furry body
G reat big footprints are left
E verybody should respect their habitat
R *oar!* Tigers roar loud!

Evie Howard (7)
Mount Nod Primary School, Coventry

Shark

S harks have very sharp teeth
H oming in on their prey
A pproaching carefully, sniffing blood
R acing, rushing, that's what sharks do
K ings of the sea, they are.

Isaac Mills (7)
Mount Nod Primary School, Coventry

Dinosaur

D ifferent
I nteresting
N aughty
O range
S miley
A mazing
U nbelievable
R oars!

Jai Singh Kaila (6)
Mount Nod Primary School, Coventry

Unicorn

U nicorn
N ice
I nteresting
C ute
O range tail
R eal unicorn
N ight unicorn.

Nishān Kaur Kaila (6)
Mount Nod Primary School, Coventry

Crab

C reepy crawly crabs
R uby-red shells
A ll live together
B y the sea and the sand.

Leah Allchurch (5)
Mount Nod Primary School, Coventry

Cat

C uddly and loving
A ctive and crazy
T he cat next door is very lazy.

Jenson Cole (6)
Mount Nod Primary School, Coventry

I Love Unicorn

I am Sanya.

L ove is a beautiful feeling
O n my dream, I saw a unicorn
V ery beautiful, blue-coloured unicorn
E ating my chocolate cake :(

U nicorn with his horn on his head
N odding my feet
I t tickles me, and makes me smile
C uddling me for a while
O n his back, he takes me for a ride
R iding along the beach
N ight deepens, makes me fall asleep.

Sanya Khatri (5)
Pelham Primary School, Bexleyheath

Unicorn's Rainbow Magic

U nicorns are rare and magical creatures
N ot to be mistaken for a white horse
I ts powerful, spiralling horn
C an make you happy
O r heal your heart with glitter, the place where a
R ainbow touches the ground is where you'll find them
N earby the mermaids, elves and woodland fairies.

Mila Dhesi (4)
Pelham Primary School, Bexleyheath

Dolphin

D iving in the sea
O cean living
L ong noses
P lay together
H igh-pitched
I ntelligent mammals
N ot fish, they are mammals.

Jack Brown (4)
Pelham Primary School, Bexleyheath

Super Fast

T igers are super fast and strong, they hunt with their sharp teeth
I don't think anyone can catch them because they are super fast with their muscles
G roan, groan, groan, they always moan
E at, they always need to eat, that's how they get strong
R *oar, roar, roar!* They sound so loud.

Sienna Walker (7)
Perry Court E-ACT Academy, Hengrove

Flamingo

F ish is what they eat
L akes are where they live
A flamingo is pink
M ummy flamingos leave their babies in the nest
I have 'Mingo the Flamingo' - it is a book
N o babies are pink
G o to a lake, you might find one
O n a nest, an egg will lie.

Bonnie Firks (7)
Perry Court E-ACT Academy, Hengrove

Puppy

P uppies are cute and they love a treat
U nder my bed, she lies by my feet
P oppy is her name, fetch is her favourite game
P oop, poop, poop, it's everywhere
Y ikes! I've stood in it! That's not fair!

Miley McSweeney (7)
Perry Court E-ACT Academy, Hengrove

Deer

D elightful, beautiful deer
E veryone likes deer
E ars are fluffy and pointy
R ivers in the forest where deer live, with spots on their back and on their face and legs.

Layla Stuckes (6)
Perry Court E-ACT Academy, Hengrove

Hyenas

H ave black eyes
Y ou would not outrun one
E at meat
N ever go near one
A ttack or you will die
S ee one, it will bite.

Joelle Forbes (6)
Perry Court E-ACT Academy, Hengrove

Gecko

G reen, rough, small
E at lovely insects
C amouflaged and colourful
K ind of fun to see
O n the move but can't see.

Eva Massaro (6)
Perry Court E-ACT Academy, Hengrove

Leopards

L eopards are the strongest of the big cats
E very leopard has 1,200 spots
O ne reason why leopards take their prey into a tree is to keep it safe from lions
P erhaps you will never see one because it is camouflaged
A nd I wish I could see one today
R ainforests, mountains and savannahs are all habitats of leopards
D ue to the leopard's superlative stealthiness, people often remain unaware that big cats live in nearby areas
S ome leopards love to play with their cubs whilst waiting for prey in the long grass.

Ella Fosberry (7)
Richard Hill CE Primary School, Thurcaston

Amur Leopard

A mazing leopards, clever and smart
M aking them happy is close to my heart
U nseen round the forest, hidden by their spots
R unning wild, having fun in the sun

L oving leopards for me is number one
E very leopard is great in a spectacular way
O h, how I wish to see one one day
P rowling, powerful predator
A ll the other animals are scared of this thing
R eady to pounce, tensed to jump
D aring and quiet, you won't hear him spring.

Bethany Kendall (7)
Richard Hill CE Primary School, Thurcaston

Rottweiler

R ottweilers are cute and vicious
O ur protector
T o keep our house safe
T o lick our faces and bite people
W alking through the field is nice for them
E at my food when I don't want it
I am a vicious dog, I can be nice if you are
L icks all over your face from me
E very time I see you after school
R eggy, I love you, and you boys are the best!

Noah Jackson (7)
Richard Hill CE Primary School, Thurcaston

My Dog Holly

M y dog is a boxador
Y es, she is very cute

D idn't take her long to chew through my dad's boot
O nly three months old
G ot a tail like a whip

H olly loves tug of war and has an epic grip
O utside is her favourite place
L ovely walks our family takes
L ying in her bed for a rest
Y es, my dog is simply the best!

Jacob Bailey (6)
Richard Hill CE Primary School, Thurcaston

Mountain Lion

M ountain is one of its habitats
O n mountains
U nder threat almost
N ature
T eams up with cubs
A nimal
I n rainforests
N aughty

L east concern
I n deserts
O n hills
N ever going extinct.

Finn Baker (6)
Richard Hill CE Primary School, Thurcaston

Picking Out The Panda Facts

P eople in China are working hard to increase panda numbers
A ll pandas are like fluffy footballs rolling around
N othing beats a fresh bamboo stick
D id you know that pandas can swim?
A dult pandas can weigh up to 150kg!

Oscar Bower (7)
Richard Hill CE Primary School, Thurcaston

Antelope

A ntlers
N ot extinct, but endangered
T hey hide their babies in long grass
E at grass
L ions eat them
O ften in Asia and Africa
P eople hunt them
E ven-toed.

Zak Foster (7)
Richard Hill CE Primary School, Thurcaston

Cuddly Koala

K oala means 'no drink'
O ur favourite food is leaves from the eucalyptus tree
A ustralia is our home
L azy koalas sleep for eighteen hours a day
A wesomely cuddly.

Lola Fletcher (7)
Richard Hill CE Primary School, Thurcaston

Eagles

E agles fly so fast
A cross the great big sky
G liding up and down like an aeroplane
L oving flying high
E asily turning
S oaring across the sky.

Joshua Little (7)
Richard Hill CE Primary School, Thurcaston

Lion

L ying in the savannah
I n a group called a pride
O strich, zebra and buffalo are on the menu
N ew babies are called cubs.

Madison Burbidge (6)
Richard Hill CE Primary School, Thurcaston

My Dog

F un Finley
I s great
N ice licks
L oves cuddles
E ats treats
Y ummy in my tummy.

Isobel Richardson (6)
Richard Hill CE Primary School, Thurcaston

Save The World!

O wls are sweet
W hat is now? What about an owl?
L ove omnivore owls, sometimes they're on the ground.

Bella Culleton (7)
Richard Hill CE Primary School, Thurcaston

Unicorn

U nicorns are my favourite
N ibbling holly leaves
I have never seen one
C an they really be true?
O r are they magic with their
R ainbow tail and mane
N icely in a plait?

Mathilda Jewitt (5)
Singleton CE Primary School, Singleton

My Rainbow Sparkle Unicorn

U nique, magical horse
N ice and beautiful
I nviting princesses
C arrying them
O ne horn and wings
R unning fast to
N everland!

Gretta Mills (4)
Singleton CE Primary School, Singleton

Unicorn

U nbelievable horn
N ight-time thing
I nto the night
C olourful mane
O f gold and silver
R ainbow mane
N ever stops shining.

Noah North (5)
Singleton CE Primary School, Singleton

Dog

D oggy
O ld
G ood.

Arthur (6)
Singleton CE Primary School, Singleton

Rainbow Pony

R ainbow pony, what a beautiful name
A treasure of colours
I t sparkles like a star
N ew every day, like a bright sun
B eautiful like the colours of the rainbow
O riginal elegance that you will never lose
W onderful tail high and bright, made of light.

P owerful colours, rich and bright
O nly one of its kind - unique
N umerous talents for us to enjoy
Y ou are a rainbow, my beautiful pony.

Jayrell K. Agyapong (6)
St Chad's RC Primary School, South Norwood

Snake, Is It Scary For Being Scaly?

S lithers from side to side while making the hiss sound
N ot everybody likes this scaly reptile
A s a pet, others find snakes as similar to our furry friends
K ids should learn facts about this legless creature
E nding the fear and to start liking this animal's unusual features.

Rocio Navarro (7)
St Chad's RC Primary School, South Norwood

Just A Giraffe

G iraffes' necks are long
I nteresting animals with spots
R unning as fast as they can
A lways hungry and eating leaves
F ast at running and with
F lexible necks they can drink from the ground
E yes on their head, so they can see.

Natalia Gorka (5)
St Chad's RC Primary School, South Norwood

Elephant

E xtremely big ears I have
L ong, pointed nose
E veryone is smaller than me
P rotective of my little ones
H ave very big feet
A frica and Asia you can find me
N ow guess who I am
T runks and tusks will give you a clue.

Angel Ava Agyekum (6)
St Chad's RC Primary School, South Norwood

Giraffe's First Adventure

G reat, long neck
I 'm very tall
R unning
A cross the land to
F ind some trees
F aster, faster
E xcited to find adventure.

Chanelle Appiah Arhin (5)
St Chad's RC Primary School, South Norwood

Cat

C aught me in the act, so what?
A shamed, I am not, who cares!
T argeting animals of prey is my hobby, ha ha ha, bye!

Jessica Anene (5)
St Chad's RC Primary School, South Norwood

Unicorns

U nicorns are beautiful
N otice how they fly
I magine their colourful tails
C oursing through the sky
O ver the trees and mountains
R iding through the clouds
N ever mind rain and snow
S ee people cheer out loud.

Jaime Blanch (6)
St George's School Edgbaston, Edgbaston

The Amazing Wombats!

W ibbling and wobbling across the grass
O h no! Where's my burrow?
M ust dig deeper
B ackwards facing pouch to keep joey warm
A nd safe from the dingos
T he sun is shining, it's time for bed.

Sophia Buray (7)
St George's School Edgbaston, Edgbaston

Unicorn

L ovely animal
O f the sky
V ery colourful
I nteresting
N ice
G orgeous creature.

Yuna Isobe (5)
St George's School Edgbaston, Edgbaston

Fish

F ish, you find them in rivers, lakes and oceans
I magine colours, many are red, green and blue
S mall and big, swim in a school
H ide under rocks, seaweed, plants and sand.

Khaeleam Darlington (7)
St Mary's Lewisham CE Primary School, Lewisham

Lions

L ions are big cats
I n the jungle
O ther animals are scared
N o one can fight lions
S tay away from lions.

Te'Amo Williams-Dythe (5)
St Mary's Lewisham CE Primary School, Lewisham

Dragon

D estroy a home, dragon!
R ide a dragon
A naughty dragon
G rowl like a bear
O hh... you dragon, you're scary!
N o, dragon!

Pola Sochacka (6)
St Michael's RC Primary School, Pillgwenlly

Dragon

D ragons drink water
R uin buildings
A rgh! Dragon!
G ood dragon, sad dragon - argh!
O h no, not my house!
N ooo! Not my house!

Theo Scarpato-Hughes (7)
St Michael's RC Primary School, Pillgwenlly

Dragon

D estroy buildings
R uin houses
A ttack people
G uard castles
O h, that's a big dragon!
N o, that's a giant dragon!

Lithongo Ndololwana (7)
St Michael's RC Primary School, Pillgwenlly

Dragon

D ragons can attack
R oar loudly, dragons
A big dragon is coming
G et off me, dragon!
O ff you go!
N asty dragon!

Mateusz Ukrynczuk (7)
St Michael's RC Primary School, Pillgwenlly

Rüppell's Vulture

V ery fast, eats carrion
U nder thick brown feathers, stays dry
L appet-faced vultures are less rare
T alons on toes sharp and long
U p in the sky, the highest flyer
R ips flesh with a hooked beak
E yelids, they're like windscreen wipers.

Jacob Bainbridge (5)
St Peter's CE (A) Primary School, Caverswall

Chicken

C hickens are fluffy
H ave spikes on their legs
I n and out of bushes
C ute as can be
K icking and scratching the ground
E ating whatever they find
N o worm or bug is safe!

Archie Walker (6)
St Peter's CE (A) Primary School, Caverswall

Crab

C reatures crawling on the ocean shore
R ooting around for food to eat
A round and around they dig in the sand
B etween the rock pool, shells and in the sea.

Kaiden Rushton (6)
St Peter's CE (A) Primary School, Caverswall

Pinchy Crabs

C licking crabs
R unning on the sand
A round the rock pools
B ashing their tummies
S harp snippers pinching and snapping.

Benjamin Coggan (6)
St Peter's CE (A) Primary School, Caverswall

Lucy The Doggy

D ogs are cute and
O ften eat food and
G o for walks and
G o in the garden. Lucy loves
Y ou and me.

Maisy Hague (5)
St Peter's CE (A) Primary School, Caverswall

My Black Cat

M idnight-black
Y awning lazily in the sun

B ut suddenly the game is on!
L eaping to her feet
A nd sprinting through the hedge
C atching her prey in one
K ill it quick, you've won!

C ats are curious creatures
A ffectionate and warm
T ill they spy a mouse, be warned

Megan Dawes (6)
St Peter's CIW Primary School, Rossett

Luna Loves To Eat

L una the Labrador is a puppy
A nd she wants to eat the world
B reakfast and dinner are not enough
R eally, she just wants peanut butter
A nd cheese
D uring the day, she likes to play
O r have cuddles and eat more
R eally yummy treats.

Zoe Sutherland (7)
St Peter's CIW Primary School, Rossett

Unicorn

U p in the sky, unicorns fly
N *eigh* is the noise unicorns make
I n the light, their colours glisten
C olourful, magical, but they don't listen!
O ver and under the rainbow
R unning through the clouds
N ow do you think it's real?

Lillie Walsh (7)
St Peter's CIW Primary School, Rossett

Silly Horses

H orseshoes on, ready to go
O utside is our favourite place
R unning in fields, fast or slow
S illy horses, go, go, go!
E ating hay
S leepy in our stables, *neigh, neigh, neigh.*

Harry Bueruer (6)
St Peter's CIW Primary School, Rossett

Tigers Don't Drink Tea

T igers don't drink tea
I t's not tasty
G rowling and
E ating is more fun
R elaxing ends the day.

Jack Yiend (6)
St Peter's CIW Primary School, Rossett

Spider

S piders are black
P laying on webs
I nsect, crawls
D own it goes
E ight legs
R ough to rub.

Zoe Hall (8)
Thomas Wolsey Ormiston Academy, Ipswich

T-Rex

T -rex is big
R oar is the noise they make
E at meat, yum!
X ylophones they like to play.

Jay Walters (8)
Thomas Wolsey Ormiston Academy, Ipswich

Dog

D ark and bark outside
O range, soft, smooth
G ive cuddles, hairy.

Chloe Barden (6)
Thomas Wolsey Ormiston Academy, Ipswich

Fish

F ast flip
I cy
S wims, wet
H as bubbles.

Alice Wade (9)
Thomas Wolsey Ormiston Academy, Ipswich

Snakes And Their Babies

S lither all around the ground
N ice but scary
A dult snakes are bigger than baby snakes
K eep touch with their babies
E at meat and not plants.

Lillia Yau (6)
Whitehouse Primary School, Elm Tree

Jaguar

J aguars can jump very high
A jaguar can run very fast
G iant
U nbelievable
A jaguar is fast
R eally, really speedy.

Thomas Amos (5)
Whitehouse Primary School, Elm Tree

Jaguar

J aguars can jump very high
A jaguar can run very fast
G iant!
U nbelievable
A jaguar is speedy
R eally speedy!

Jacob Ragan (5)
Whitehouse Primary School, Elm Tree

Jaguar

J aguars can run the fastest in the cat family
A mazing
G iant!
U nbelievable
A nd speedy
R eally, really fast!

Noah Wassell (5)
Whitehouse Primary School, Elm Tree

Parrots

P arrots have long tails
A parrot is colourful
R un really fast
R ainbow
O range feathers
T hey can dive fast.

Ted Swainston (6)
Whitehouse Primary School, Elm Tree

Jaguar

J aguars jump very high
A jaguar is enormous
G iant
U nbelievable
A mazing
R eally scary and the fastest cat.

Haider Ali Khan (5)
Whitehouse Primary School, Elm Tree

Leopard

L ong legs
E normous teeth
O range eyes
P ointy claws
A ngry eyes
R oaring noise
D angerous.

Noah McDonald (6)
Whitehouse Primary School, Elm Tree

Toucan

T errific wings
O range beak
U nbelievable face
C olourful eyes
A dorable bird
N ice and friendly.

Isaac Fixter (5)
Whitehouse Primary School, Elm Tree

Parrot

P ointy yellow beak
A nnoying noises
R ed feathers
R ainbow wings
O range claws
T eeny round eyes.

Isla Archment (5)
Whitehouse Primary School, Elm Tree

Sloths

S loths are clever at climbing
L ots of being lazy
O range
T rying to be good
H ides when people are coming.

Georgie Huskinson-Williams (5)
Whitehouse Primary School, Elm Tree

Parrot

P retty silly
A mazing feathers
R ed beak
R ainbow feathers
O range head
T alks, is clever.

Emily Buttle (6)
Whitehouse Primary School, Elm Tree

Jaguar

J et-black fur
A ngry eyes
G iant paws
U nkind to its prey
A ngry and scary
R apid legs.

Zayn-Ali Ayoub (6)
Whitehouse Primary School, Elm Tree

Swimming Shark

S harks have sharp teeth
H ave small teeth
A re very dangerous
R eally dangerous
K eep away!

Billy (7)
Whitehouse Primary School, Elm Tree

Tiger

T here he is
I n trees for black stripes
G rowling really loud
E vil, scary
R eally fast!

Hafeez Khan (6)
Whitehouse Primary School, Elm Tree

Tiger

T errible sharp teeth
I ncredible strength
G iant paws
E vil eyes
R ough and fierce.

Leo Atkinson (5)
Whitehouse Primary School, Elm Tree

Parrot

P retty
A parrot is colourful
R ed
R ainbow
O range
T hey fly.

Dominic White (6), Daisy & Reece Fletcher (5)
Whitehouse Primary School, Elm Tree

Sloths

S loths are sleepy
L azy and lovely
O range
T ruly lazy
H airy and silly.

Alec Fixter (5)
Whitehouse Primary School, Elm Tree

Sloth

S loths have long arms
L azy and tired
O range and brown
T ired
H airy.

Teddy Moore (6)
Whitehouse Primary School, Elm Tree

Parrot

P retty
A mazing
R ed
R eally silly
O range
T alks.

Lucy Coyne (5)
Whitehouse Primary School, Elm Tree

Sloth

S leep in the night
L ie down
O range and brown
T ired
H airy.

Jake Cordiner (5)
Whitehouse Primary School, Elm Tree

Frog

F unny feet
R ound big eyes
O range, soft body
G reat at jumping high.

Phrel Oketunde (6)
Whitehouse Primary School, Elm Tree

Tiger

T all
I nteresting
G reat
E normous
R ed.

Macie Graham (5)
Whitehouse Primary School, Elm Tree

Steggy The Stegosaurus

S trong muscles are what makes Steggy
T ough, armoured body to protect himself
E normous plates down its back
G obbling up all the leaves
O nly a stegosaurus can defeat an allosaurus
S hort in height, but long in length
A ll stegosaurus have spiky tails
U nlikely to win a race with its big, round belly
R oofed lizard is what stegosaurus means
U SA is where my fossils were found in 1982
S tinkysaurus is my nickname because of all that vegetation.

Bhavraj Sokhal (6)
Woodlands School, Great Warley

Elephants In The Wild

E lephants have long trunks so they can wash their bodies and feed themselves
L ikes to eat lots of green leaves
E njoys playing in water with friends and family
P lays in the mud to keep cool
H ot countries are where they mostly live
A frican elephants have the largest ears
N aughty people kill elephants to cut off their tusks
T heir trunks are long and strong.

Millie Patel (6)
Woodlands School, Great Warley

My Rabbit Cocoa

C uddly Cocoa
O utside and in
C uddly Cocoa, I love him
O h, how soft his fur can be
A crobatic Cocoa loves me.

Leo Sheringham (6)
Woodlands School, Great Warley

The Mischievous Floppy Dog

D uke, my dog, is so mischievous
O bedient when I'm with him and
G rowling on my mum's conversation.

Kiaran Pagotre (7)
Woodlands School, Great Warley

Beartastic

B ig, bold bear
E nergetic energy
A nd small cubs are adorable
R unning wild in the forest.

Veer Singh Virk (6)
Woodlands School, Great Warley

Young Writers Information

We hope you have enjoyed reading this book – and that you will continue to in the coming years.

If you're a young writer who enjoys reading and creative writing, or the parent of an enthusiastic poet or story writer, do visit our website **www.youngwriters.co.uk**. Here you will find free competitions, workshops and games, as well as recommended reads, a poetry glossary and our blog. There's lots to keep budding writers motivated to write!

If you would like to order further copies of this book, or any of our other titles, then please give us a call or order via your online account.

Young Writers
Remus House
Coltsfoot Drive
Peterborough
PE2 9BF
(01733) 890066
info@youngwriters.co.uk

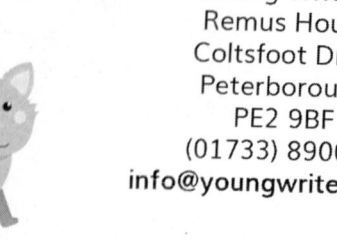

Join in the conversation!
Tips, news, giveaways and much more!

YoungWritersUK   @YoungWritersCW